# Icarus,
## he Boy Who Flew

First published in 2008 by
Franklin Watts
338 Euston Road
London
NW1 3BH

Franklin Watts Australia
Level 17/207 Kent Street
Sydney
NSW 2000

A CIP catalogue record for this book is available
from the British Library.

ISBN 978 0 7496 7992 7 (hbk)
ISBN 978 0 7496 8000 8 (pbk)

**Series Editor:** Melanie Palmer
**Series Advisor:** Dr Barrie Wade
**Series Designer:** Peter Scoulding

Printed in China

Franklin Watts is a division of
Hachette Children's Books,
an Hachette Livre UK company
www.hachettelivre.co.uk

# Icarus,
## the Boy Who Flew

by Barrie Wade and David Lopez

FRANKLIN WATTS
LONDON • SYDNEY

Long ago Icarus lived
with his father, Daedalus.
Daedalus was a great inventor.

One day the king asked Daedalus to build him a giant maze. It was to hide a terrible secret.

So Daedalus built the biggest maze anyone had ever seen.

The king was delighted. But he locked Daedalus and Icarus in a prison tower. They knew the king's secret, so they could never leave.

Birds came to eat the crumbs that Icarus left by the window. Then, as the birds flew away, a few feathers floated down.

"I wish I was as free as a bird,"
Icarus said sadly. Daedalus smiled.
"I have a plan," he said.

"Help me collect these feathers
until we have enough to fly!"
Daedulus said. So Icarus found
as many as he could.

Daedalus worked for many
months. He tied the feathers
together with thread. Then he
stuck them down with candle wax.

At last, Daedalus finished. He had made two huge pairs of wings.

"Let's go now!" cried Icarus.

He longed to fly out of the tower.

"All right, my son," said his
father. "But remember not to fly
too low, or the sea spray will make
your wings wet and heavy.

"Don't fly too high either,
or the sun will melt them."
"Yes Father," said Icarus, but
he wasn't really listening.

Iacrus longed to fly like a bird.
He went up to the window and
jumped out, with Daedalus close
behind him.

Icarus flapped his wings – he could fly! He felt the rush of air as he flew. "I'm free!" he shouted.

He could glide ...

and he could dive!

"Icarus! Not too low!" his father
shouted. Icarus remembered the
sea spray and flapped his wings.

He climbed in circles, higher and
higher into the light. This was
even better than diving!

Daedalus was shouting below but
Icarus was too high to hear him.

Higher and higher soared Icarus, dizzy with excitement.

Then he remembered the sun –
but it was too late!

The wax was already melting.

Feathers began to fall off.

Icarus dived down to cooler air. His feathers fell away like flower petals. Down and down he fell.

Like a stone he dropped into the sea. His father watched helplessly.

For a moment a few feathers
floated like foam on the water,
then sank. Icarus was lost forever.

Daedalus threw his wings away.

He never flew again.

Hopscotch has been specially designed to fit the requirements of the Literacy Framework. It offers real books by top authors and illustrators for children developing their reading skills. There are 63 Hopscotch stories to choose from:

**Marvin, the Blue Pig**
ISBN 978 0 7496 4619 6

**Plip and Plop**
ISBN 978 0 7496 4620 2

**The Queen's Dragon**
ISBN 978 0 7496 4618 9

**Flora McQuack**
ISBN 978 0 7496 4621 9

**Willie the Whale**
ISBN 978 0 7496 4623 3

**Naughty Nancy**
ISBN 978 0 7496 4622 6

**Run!**
ISBN 978 0 7496 4705 6

**The Playground Snake**
ISBN 978 0 7496 4706 3

**"Sausages!"**
ISBN 978 0 7496 4707 0

**Bear in Town**
ISBN 978 0 7496 5875 5

**Pippin's Big Jump**
ISBN 978 0 7496 4710 0

**Whose Birthday Is It?**
ISBN 978 0 7496 4709 4

**The Princess and the Frog**
ISBN 978 0 7496 5129 9

**Flynn Flies High**
ISBN 978 0 7496 5130 5

**Clever Cat**
ISBN 978 0 7496 5131 2

**Moo!**
ISBN 978 0 7496 5332 3

**Izzie's Idea**
ISBN 978 0 7496 5334 7

**Roly-poly Rice Ball**
ISBN 978 0 7496 5333 0

**I Can't Stand It!**
ISBN 978 0 7496 5765 9

**Cockerel's Big Egg**
ISBN 978 0 7496 5767 3

**How to Teach a Dragon Manners**
ISBN 978 0 7496 5873 1

**The Truth about those Billy Goats**
ISBN 978 0 7496 5766 6

**Marlowe's Mum and the Tree House**
ISBN 978 0 7496 5874 8

**The Truth about Hansel and Gretel**
ISBN 978 0 7496 4708 7

**The Best Den Ever**
ISBN 978 0 7496 5876 2

## ADVENTURES

**Aladdin and the Lamp**
ISBN 978 0 7496 6692 7

**Blackbeard the Pirate**
ISBN 978 0 7496 6690 3

**George and the Dragon**
ISBN 978 0 7496 6691 0

**Jack the Giant-Killer**
ISBN 978 0 7496 6693 4

## TALES OF KING ARTHUR

**1. The Sword in the Stone**
ISBN 978 0 7496 6694 1

**2. Arthur the King**
ISBN 978 0 7496 6695 8

**3. The Round Table**
ISBN 978 0 7496 6697 2

**4. Sir Lancelot and the Ice Castle**
ISBN 978 0 7496 6698 9

## TALES OF ROBIN HOOD

**Robin and the Knight**
ISBN 978 0 7496 6699 6

**Robin and the Monk**
ISBN 978 0 7496 6700 9

**Robin and the Silver Arrow**
ISBN 978 0 7496 6703 0

**Robin and the Friar**
ISBN 978 0 7496 6702 3

## FAIRY TALES

**The Emperor's New Clothes**
ISBN 978 0 7496 7421 2

**Cinderella**
ISBN 978 0 7496 7417 5

**Snow White**
ISBN 978 0 7496 7418 2

**Jack and the Beanstalk**
ISBN 978 0 7496 7422 9

**The Three Billy Goats Gruff**
ISBN 978 0 7496 7420 5

**The Pied Piper of Hamelin**
ISBN 978 0 7496 7419 9

**Goldilocks and the Three Bears**
ISBN 978 0 7496 7903 3

**Hansel and Gretel**
ISBN 978 0 7496 7904 0

**The Three Little Pigs**
ISBN 978 0 7496 7905 7

**Rapunzel**
ISBN 978 0 7496 7906 4

**Little Red Riding Hood**
ISBN 978 0 7496 7907 1

**Rumpelstiltskin**
ISBN 978 0 7496 7908 8

## HISTORIES

**Toby and the Great Fire of London**
ISBN 978 0 7496 7410 6

**Pocahontas the Peacemaker**
ISBN 978 0 7496 7411 3

**Grandma's Seaside Bloomers**
ISBN 978 0 7496 7412 0

**Hoorah for Mary Seacole**
ISBN 978 0 7496 7413 7

**Remember the 5th of November**
ISBN 978 0 7496 7414 4

**Tutankhamun and the Golden Chariot**
ISBN 978 0 7496 7415 1

## MYTHS

**Icarus, the Boy Who Flew**
ISBN 978 0 7496 7992 7 *
ISBN 978 0 7496 8000 8

**Perseus and the Snake Monster**
ISBN 978 0 7496 7993 4 *
ISBN 978 0 7496 8001 5

**Odysseus and the Wooden Horse**
ISBN 978 0 7496 7994 1 *
ISBN 978 0 7496 8002 2

**Persephone and the Pomegranate Seeds**
ISBN 978 0 7496 7995 8 *
ISBN 978 0 7496 8003 9

**Romulus and Remus**
ISBN 978 0 7496 7996 5 *
ISBN 978 0 7496 8004 6

**Thor's Hammer**
ISBN 978 0 7496 7997 2*
ISBN 978 0 7496 8005 3

**No Dinner for Anansi**
ISBN 978 0 7496 7998 9 *
ISBN 978 0 7496 8006 0

**Gelert the Brave**
ISBN 978 0 7496 7999 6*
ISBN 978 0 7496 8007 7

* **hardback**